From Waste to Wonder: The

Paolo Rossi

Copyright © [2023]

Author: Paolo Rossi

Title: From Waste to Wonder: The Power of Recycling

This book is a product of [Publisher's Paolo Rossi]

ISBN:

TABLE OF CONTENTS

Chapter 1: The Environmental Crisis

Understanding the Global Waste Problem

The Impact of Waste on Ecosystems

The Role of Recycling in Environmental Conservation

Chapter 2: The Importance of Recycling

Reducing Landfill Waste

Conserving Natural Resources

Preventing Pollution and Climate Change

Chapter 3: Recycling Basics

Sorting and Segregating Waste

Understanding Different Types of Recyclables

Recycling Methods and Processes

Chapter 4: The Economic Benefits of Recycling 25

Job Creation and Economic Growth

Cost Savings for Municipalities and Businesses

Promoting Sustainable Industries

Chapter 5: Recycling Around the World 31

Successful Recycling Programs and Initiatives

Challenges and Solutions in Developing Countries

Global Collaboration for a Sustainable Future

Chapter 6: Innovations in Recycling Technology 38

Advanced Sorting and Processing Techniques

Creative Upcycling and Repurposing Ideas

Emerging Technologies and Future Possibilities

Chapter 7: Recycling at Home and in the Community

Setting up an Effective Recycling System at Home

Engaging Schools and Local Organizations in Recycling

Promoting a Culture of Sustainability

Chapter 8: Overcoming Barriers to Recycling

Lack of Awareness and Education

Addressing Behavioral and Attitudinal Challenges

Policy and Legislative Support for Recycling Efforts

Chapter 9: Inspiring Stories of Recycling Success

Individuals Making a Difference

Businesses Leading the Way

Community-driven Recycling Initiatives

Chapter 10: The Future of Recycling 62

Innovations and Breakthroughs on the Horizon

Shifting Towards a Circular Economy

Creating a Sustainable Legacy for Future Generations

Conclusion: Empowering Change through Recycling 68

Chapter 1: The Environmental Crisis

Understanding the Global Waste Problem

The world is facing a massive waste problem, and it is high time we all understand the gravity of the situation. This subchapter aims to shed light on the global waste crisis and its implications for everyone. Whether you are an environmental enthusiast or someone who is new to the concept of recycling, it is crucial to grasp the importance of addressing this issue collectively.

The global waste problem is not limited to a specific region or country; it is a challenge that affects every corner of the world. Every year, billions of tons of waste accumulate, filling up landfills and polluting our oceans, rivers, and forests. The consequences of this rampant waste generation are dire and impact the environment, human health, and the economy.

One of the most alarming aspects of the global waste problem is the sheer volume of waste being generated. As the world population continues to grow, so does our consumption, leading to an exponential increase in waste production. This unsustainable pattern of consumption and disposal is putting an immense strain on the planet's resources and ecosystems.

Furthermore, the improper disposal of waste has severe environmental consequences. Landfills emit harmful greenhouse gases, contributing to climate change. Plastics and other non-biodegradable materials find their way into our oceans, causing irreversible damage to marine life and ecosystems. The contamination of soil and water due to hazardous waste poses a significant threat to human health and biodiversity.

Understanding the global waste problem also requires recognizing the economic implications. The cost of managing and disposing of waste is a burden on governments and local communities. Moreover, valuable resources are being wasted when materials that could be recycled or reused end up in landfills. Recycling not only helps conserve resources but also creates job opportunities and stimulates economic growth.

As individuals, we all have a role to play in addressing the global waste problem. By embracing the importance of recycling, we can contribute to reducing waste, conserving resources, and protecting the environment. Recycling helps to minimize the need for raw materials extraction and energy consumption, resulting in reduced greenhouse gas emissions.

In conclusion, the global waste problem is a pressing issue that affects every one of us. Understanding its gravity and implications is the first step towards finding sustainable solutions. By recognizing the importance of recycling, we can actively participate in creating a world where waste is transformed into wonder, benefiting both the environment and our future generations.

The Impact of Waste on Ecosystems

In our modern society, waste has become an ever-increasing problem that poses a significant threat to our delicate ecosystems. From plastic bottles to electronic waste, our careless disposal habits have led to devastating consequences that affect not only the environment but also the well-being of all living organisms. This subchapter explores the profound impact of waste on ecosystems and emphasizes the urgent need for recycling as a solution.

One of the most alarming effects of waste on ecosystems is the pollution of our waterways. When non-biodegradable waste enters rivers, lakes, and oceans, it disrupts the balance of aquatic ecosystems. Marine life, such as fish, turtles, and seabirds, mistakes plastic debris for food, resulting in countless deaths due to ingestion or entanglement. Additionally, toxic chemicals from household waste and industries contaminate water sources, poisoning aquatic organisms and disrupting the entire food chain.

Land ecosystems are equally affected by waste mismanagement. Improper disposal of waste in landfills releases harmful greenhouse gases, contributing to climate change. Moreover, as landfills continue to overflow, toxins seep into the soil and find their way into plants, animals, and eventually, humans. This contamination can lead to serious health issues, including respiratory problems, cancer, and birth defects.

Furthermore, waste has a direct impact on biodiversity. As habitats are destroyed to make way for landfills or incinerators, countless species lose their homes and are pushed towards extinction. Additionally, the production and extraction of raw materials to meet the demands of our consumer-driven society further degrade natural habitats, exacerbating the loss of biodiversity.

To combat these detrimental effects, it is crucial that we embrace the importance of recycling. Recycling not only reduces waste sent to landfills but also conserves natural resources and reduces greenhouse gas emissions. By recycling materials such as paper, glass, plastic, and metals, we can significantly decrease the negative impact on ecosystems. Additionally, recycling electronic waste, which contains hazardous materials like lead and mercury, prevents these toxins from leaching into the environment.

The power of recycling lies in its ability to transform waste into valuable resources. By reusing materials, we can reduce the need for extracting virgin resources, preserving natural habitats and biodiversity. Recycling also supports a circular economy, where the life cycle of products is extended, reducing waste generation and promoting sustainability.

In conclusion, waste has a profound impact on ecosystems, threatening the delicate balance of our environment and the well-being of all living organisms. Recognizing the importance of recycling and actively participating in it is essential for mitigating these effects. By embracing recycling as a powerful tool, we can turn waste into wonder, preserving our planet and ensuring a sustainable future for generations to come.

The Role of Recycling in Environmental Conservation

The Importance of Recycling has been a topic of increasing concern in recent years, as we grapple with the consequences of our excessive consumption and waste generation. Recycling, as a key component of environmental conservation, plays a crucial role in mitigating the detrimental impacts on our planet. In this subchapter, we will delve into the various ways in which recycling contributes to safeguarding our environment.

First and foremost, recycling helps to reduce the extraction of raw materials from the Earth. By reusing materials such as paper, glass, plastic, and metal, we can significantly decrease the need for new resources. This not only conserves natural habitats and ecosystems but also helps to preserve the delicate balance of the Earth's biodiversity. Additionally, recycling reduces the energy required for the manufacturing process, thereby lowering greenhouse gas emissions and combating climate change.

Another vital aspect of recycling is waste reduction. Landfills are rapidly filling up, polluting the soil, water, and air. By diverting waste materials from landfills through recycling, we can alleviate the strain on these already overwhelmed disposal sites. This, in turn, reduces the risk of groundwater contamination and the release of harmful gases into the atmosphere, ultimately ensuring cleaner and healthier environments for both humans and wildlife.

Furthermore, recycling plays a crucial role in the conservation of energy. It takes far less energy to recycle materials compared to extracting and processing new ones. For example, recycling aluminum cans saves up to 95% of the energy required to produce them from raw materials. By embracing recycling, we can significantly reduce our carbon footprint and conserve valuable energy resources.

Recycling also fosters a mindset of sustainability and responsibility. It encourages individuals and communities to rethink their consumption patterns and make conscious choices to reduce waste. By actively participating in recycling initiatives, we not only contribute to environmental conservation but also inspire others to follow suit, creating a ripple effect of positive change.

In conclusion, the role of recycling in environmental conservation cannot be overstated. It is a powerful tool that allows us to protect the Earth's resources, reduce waste, conserve energy, and promote sustainability. By understanding the importance of recycling and actively engaging in recycling practices, we can all contribute to a healthier and more sustainable future for ourselves and future generations.

Chapter 2: The Importance of Recycling

Reducing Landfill Waste

In today's modern world, the issue of waste management has become increasingly crucial. With the growth of population and urbanization, the amount of waste generated has reached unprecedented levels. This poses a significant threat to our environment, particularly when it comes to landfill waste. However, there is a powerful solution that can make a substantial impact - recycling.

Landfills are not just unsightly and smelly, but they also have severe environmental consequences. Organic waste decomposes and produces harmful greenhouse gases, contributing to climate change. Additionally, hazardous materials present in landfills can contaminate soil and water, posing a threat to both human health and wildlife. Therefore, reducing landfill waste is of utmost importance and can be achieved through recycling.

Recycling is the process of converting waste materials into reusable materials. By recycling, we can divert a significant portion of waste from landfills, thus reducing the environmental impact. There are various ways in which recycling helps in reducing landfill waste.

Firstly, recycling conserves natural resources. By reusing materials such as paper, plastic, metal, and glass, we reduce the demand for raw materials. This, in turn, reduces the need for destructive extraction processes, such as mining or deforestation. By recycling just one ton of paper, we can save around 17 trees, 7,000 gallons of water, and 380 gallons of oil.

Secondly, recycling reduces energy consumption. The production of new materials from recycled ones typically requires less energy compared to creating them from scratch. For example, recycling aluminum cans saves up to 95% of the energy required to produce aluminum from raw materials. This not only reduces the strain on our energy resources but also decreases greenhouse gas emissions.

Furthermore, recycling creates job opportunities and boosts the economy. The recycling industry employs millions of people worldwide, contributing to economic growth and stability. By supporting recycling initiatives, we can foster sustainable development and reduce unemployment rates.

To effectively reduce landfill waste, everyone must actively participate in recycling efforts. This involves separating recyclable materials from general waste and using designated recycling bins. Additionally, it is important to educate ourselves and others about the importance of recycling and its positive impact on the environment.

In conclusion, reducing landfill waste is a critical step towards creating a sustainable future. By embracing recycling, we can conserve natural resources, reduce energy consumption, and stimulate economic growth. Let us all join hands and be part of the recycling revolution, transforming waste into wonder. Together, we can make a significant difference and protect our planet for generations to come.

Conserving Natural Resources

In today's world, it has become increasingly important to focus on conserving natural resources. The earth provides us with a vast array of resources that are essential for our survival and well-being. From water and air to minerals and fossil fuels, these resources are finite and must be managed wisely to ensure their availability for future generations.

One of the most effective ways to conserve natural resources is through recycling. Recycling is the process of converting waste materials into new products, reducing the need for raw materials and energy consumption. By recycling, we can minimize the extraction of finite resources and reduce the strain on our environment.

The importance of recycling cannot be overstated. Firstly, it helps to alleviate the pressure on our landfills. As the global population continues to grow, so does the amount of waste generated. By recycling, we can divert a significant portion of waste from ending up in landfills, which not only take up valuable land but also release harmful gases into the atmosphere.

Secondly, recycling reduces the demand for raw materials. When we recycle materials such as paper, plastic, and aluminum, we can reduce the need for extracting virgin resources from the earth. This helps to preserve forests, conserve water, and decrease the energy required for manufacturing processes.

Furthermore, recycling plays a vital role in reducing greenhouse gas emissions. Many manufacturing processes emit substantial amounts of carbon dioxide and other greenhouse gases into the atmosphere. By recycling, we can significantly cut down on these emissions and mitigate the effects of climate change.

Recycling also conserves energy. The production of goods from recycled materials generally requires less energy compared to using raw materials. For example, recycling aluminum cans saves up to 95% of the energy needed to produce aluminum from bauxite ore. By conserving energy, we can reduce our dependence on fossil fuels and lower our carbon footprint.

In conclusion, conserving natural resources is of utmost importance for the sustainability of our planet. Recycling is a powerful tool that can help us achieve this goal. By reducing waste, minimizing the extraction of raw materials, and conserving energy, we can make a significant impact in preserving our natural resources for future generations. It is a responsibility that falls upon each and every one of us to embrace recycling as a way to transform waste into wonder.

Preventing Pollution and Climate Change

In this subchapter, we will delve into the crucial role that recycling plays in preventing pollution and mitigating climate change. As we navigate the challenges of the 21st century, it is essential for everyone to understand the importance of recycling and its direct impact on our environment and future generations.

Pollution, in all its forms, poses a significant threat to our planet. From air and water pollution to the accumulation of waste in landfills, the consequences are far-reaching. Thankfully, recycling provides a powerful solution to combat these issues. By recycling materials such as plastic, paper, glass, and metal, we can significantly reduce the amount of waste sent to landfills and incinerators. This not only prevents pollution but also conserves valuable resources and reduces the need for raw material extraction.

Furthermore, recycling plays a vital role in combating climate change. The manufacturing of products from virgin materials often results in substantial carbon emissions. However, by recycling materials, we can reduce the energy required for production and subsequently lower greenhouse gas emissions. Recycling aluminum, for instance, saves up to 95% of the energy needed to produce it from raw materials, while recycling paper can save countless trees and reduce deforestation.

By actively participating in recycling initiatives, we can all contribute to a cleaner, healthier planet. Recycling not only benefits the environment but also stimulates economic growth and job creation. It fosters the development of a circular economy, where materials are continuously recycled and reused, reducing the need for extraction and production from scratch.

To make recycling a part of our daily lives, it is crucial to educate ourselves and adopt sustainable habits. Simple steps such as separating recyclables from general waste, using reusable shopping bags, and choosing products with minimal packaging can go a long way. Additionally, supporting recycling programs and advocating for effective waste management policies can create a significant impact at the community and national levels.

Every individual has the power to make a difference. By embracing the importance of recycling, we can protect our environment, conserve resources, and combat pollution and climate change. Together, we can transform waste into wonder and create a sustainable future for ourselves and generations to come. Let us take action now and be the change our planet needs.

Chapter 3: Recycling Basics

Sorting and Segregating Waste

In today's rapidly changing world, it has become imperative for every one of us to understand the importance of recycling. Recycling is not just a mere act of separating waste; it is a powerful tool that can help transform waste into wonder. And at the heart of this process lies sorting and segregating waste.

Sorting and segregating waste is the fundamental step in the recycling process. It involves separating different types of waste materials into distinct categories, such as paper, plastic, glass, metal, and organic waste. This process ensures that each material can be recycled efficiently and effectively.

The importance of sorting and segregating waste cannot be overstated. By doing so, we can minimize contamination and increase the recycling rate. When waste is properly sorted, it becomes easier for recycling facilities to process and transform it into new products. This not only reduces the burden on our landfills but also conserves valuable resources and reduces energy consumption.

Furthermore, sorting and segregating waste allows for the recovery of valuable materials. For instance, paper can be recycled into new paper products, plastic can be transformed into useful items, and metals can be melted down and reused. By ensuring that waste is properly sorted, we can harness the potential of these materials and create a more sustainable future.

Apart from environmental benefits, sorting and segregating waste also have economic advantages. Recycling industries create job opportunities and contribute to the local economy. When waste is properly sorted, it becomes a valuable resource that can be sold to recycling facilities, generating income for individuals and communities.

To effectively sort and segregate waste, it is essential to educate and raise awareness among every one of us. We must understand the different categories of waste and how to properly dispose of them. Implementing recycling programs in schools, workplaces, and communities can help instill good recycling habits from an early age.

In conclusion, sorting and segregating waste is a vital step in the recycling process. By doing so, we can maximize the potential of waste and transform it into wonder. It not only benefits the environment by reducing landfill waste and conserving resources but also has economic advantages. Every one of us has a role to play in sorting and segregating waste, and together, we can create a greener and more sustainable future.

Understanding Different Types of Recyclables

Recycling is not just about throwing away items in a separate bin labeled "recyclables." It involves a deeper understanding of the different types of materials that can be recycled and the impact they have on the environment. In this subchapter, we will explore the diverse range of recyclables and their significance in our recycling efforts.

Plastic is one of the most commonly used materials worldwide, but its disposal poses a significant challenge. Understanding the various types of plastics and how they can be recycled is crucial. There are seven different categories of plastic, identified by a resin identification code (RIC), which can be found on the bottom of most plastic containers. These codes help determine the appropriate recycling process for each type of plastic.

Paper and cardboard are other valuable recyclable materials. They are derived from trees, which are essential for our environment. By recycling paper and cardboard products, we can reduce deforestation and minimize the energy required to produce new paper. It is important to note that certain paper products, such as glossy or wax-coated papers, cannot be recycled due to their chemical composition.

Glass is a highly recyclable material that can be melted down and repurposed indefinitely without losing its quality. It is important to separate glass by color – clear, green, and brown – as the different colors require separate recycling processes. By recycling glass, we reduce the strain on natural resources and energy consumption.

Metals, such as aluminum and steel, are infinitely recyclable. Recycling metals not only conserves energy but also reduces greenhouse gas emissions and the need for mining raw materials. It is essential to recycle metals to prevent them from ending up in landfills, where their decomposition can release harmful substances into the environment.

Organic waste, including food scraps and yard trimmings, can also be recycled. Composting is an effective method to turn organic waste into nutrient-rich soil, reducing the amount of waste sent to landfills. By composting, we not only reduce greenhouse gas emissions but also create a valuable resource for our gardens.

Understanding the different types of recyclables is crucial for everyone involved in recycling efforts. By properly identifying and separating recyclables, we can ensure they are processed correctly, reducing the strain on natural resources and minimizing environmental impact. Recycling is not just a responsibility; it is a powerful tool that can transform waste into wonder, creating a sustainable future for all.

Recycling Methods and Processes

Recycling is a powerful tool that has the potential to transform waste into wonder. Understanding the various methods and processes involved in recycling can help us make informed decisions and maximize the impact of our recycling efforts. In this subchapter, we will explore the different recycling methods and processes that contribute to the importance of recycling.

One of the most common recycling methods is known as mechanical recycling. This process involves collecting and sorting recyclable materials, such as paper, plastic, glass, and metal, and processing them into new products. The materials are cleaned, shredded, and melted down to create raw materials that can be used in the manufacturing of new goods. Mechanical recycling is a cost-effective and widely practiced method that helps reduce the demand for virgin resources while minimizing waste.

Another important recycling method is chemical recycling. While mechanical recycling is suitable for certain materials, chemical recycling is a valuable alternative for materials that are difficult to recycle mechanically. This process involves breaking down the molecular structure of the materials to produce new chemicals or fuels. Chemical recycling can tackle complex materials like mixed plastic waste, providing a solution to the growing problem of plastic pollution.

In addition to these methods, there are also specialized recycling processes that target specific materials. For example, composting is a process that converts organic waste into nutrient-rich compost, which can be used to enrich soil and support plant growth. This method is particularly important for reducing food waste and promoting sustainable agriculture.

Moreover, innovative technologies such as pyrolysis and gasification are emerging as promising recycling processes. These methods involve heating waste materials at high temperatures, resulting in the production of energy, fuels, or other valuable byproducts. These advanced technologies have the potential to transform waste into renewable energy sources, contributing to a more sustainable future.

Understanding the various recycling methods and processes is crucial in order to make informed choices and actively participate in recycling initiatives. By recycling, we conserve natural resources, reduce greenhouse gas emissions, and minimize the amount of waste that ends up in landfills or pollutes our environment. Recycling is not just a responsibility of a few, but a collective effort that can be embraced by everyone.

In conclusion, exploring the methods and processes of recycling is essential to understand the importance of recycling. Mechanical recycling, chemical recycling, composting, and advanced technologies all play vital roles in converting waste into valuable resources. By implementing these methods, we can contribute to a more sustainable and waste-free future for ourselves and future generations. Let us all join hands in the journey from waste to wonder through the power of recycling.

Chapter 4: The Economic Benefits of Recycling

Job Creation and Economic Growth

In today's increasingly interconnected world, the importance of recycling cannot be overstated. The act of recycling not only contributes to the preservation of our environment but also plays a crucial role in job creation and economic growth. This subchapter aims to shed light on the profound impact recycling can have on our society, addressing the audience of "everyone" and highlighting the niches of "The Importance of Recycling."

One of the key benefits of recycling is its potential to generate employment opportunities. As we embrace recycling practices, new industries emerge and existing ones expand, creating a demand for skilled workers. Recycling facilities require personnel to sort, process, and manage waste materials effectively. These jobs offer a diverse range of opportunities, from technicians and engineers to administrative staff and drivers. By investing in recycling programs, governments and organizations can foster job growth and reduce unemployment rates.

Furthermore, recycling initiatives stimulate economic growth by creating a sustainable market for recycled products. When we recycle materials such as paper, plastic, glass, and metal, we give them a second life and prevent the need for new raw materials. This reduces production costs for businesses and decreases their reliance on finite resources. By promoting the use of recycled materials, we create a market demand that drives innovation, encourages entrepreneurship, and fosters the development of new industries. As a result, the economy thrives, and communities benefit from increased economic activity.

In addition to job creation and economic growth, recycling also offers numerous indirect benefits. By reducing the amount of waste sent to landfills, recycling mitigates environmental pollution and conserves valuable natural resources. It helps combat climate change by reducing greenhouse gas emissions associated with the extraction and production of raw materials. Moreover, recycling often leads to cost savings for individuals, businesses, and governments, as it is often more economical to recycle materials than to produce new ones.

In conclusion, the importance of recycling extends far beyond environmental considerations. By embracing recycling practices, we can foster job creation, stimulate economic growth, and enjoy a range of indirect benefits. Governments, organizations, and individuals all have a role to play in promoting and supporting recycling initiatives. By doing so, we can transform waste into wonder and build a more sustainable and prosperous future for all.

Cost Savings for Municipalities and Businesses

Recycling is not just an environmental responsibility; it is also a smart financial decision for municipalities and businesses. In this subchapter, we will explore the significant cost savings that can be achieved through effective recycling practices. Understanding the financial benefits of recycling will not only encourage individuals to participate in recycling initiatives but also inspire municipalities and businesses to invest in recycling programs.

One of the primary cost savings for municipalities is the reduction in waste disposal fees. Landfill space is becoming scarce, and the fees associated with waste disposal are increasing rapidly. By implementing recycling programs, municipalities can divert a substantial amount of waste from landfills, thereby reducing disposal fees. This reduction in fees can result in significant savings for municipalities, which can be redirected towards other essential services and infrastructure development.

Additionally, recycling can help municipalities save on the costs of waste collection. When recyclable materials are separated from general waste at the source, the volume of waste to be collected decreases. This reduction in waste collection leads to lower fuel consumption, fewer collection vehicles on the roads, and decreased maintenance costs. These savings can be substantial, especially for larger cities with high waste generation rates.

For businesses, implementing recycling programs can also lead to substantial cost savings. Recycling reduces the amount of waste businesses send to landfill, resulting in reduced waste disposal fees.

Moreover, businesses can generate revenue by selling recyclable materials to recycling facilities. Many businesses have discovered that recycling can be a profitable venture, with some even generating enough revenue to offset their recycling program costs entirely.

Furthermore, recycling can help businesses save on raw material costs. By using recycled materials in their manufacturing processes, businesses can reduce their dependency on virgin resources, resulting in cost savings. Recycling not only conserves natural resources but also reduces the energy required for extracting, processing, and transporting raw materials, leading to additional cost savings.

In conclusion, cost savings are a significant advantage of recycling for both municipalities and businesses. By implementing effective recycling programs, municipalities can reduce waste disposal fees, save on waste collection costs, and redirect funds towards other essential services. Businesses, on the other hand, can benefit from reduced waste disposal fees, generate revenue from selling recyclable materials, and save on raw material costs. These financial benefits not only make recycling an environmentally responsible choice but also a financially prudent one. It is crucial for everyone, including individuals, municipalities, and businesses, to recognize the importance of recycling and actively participate in recycling initiatives for a sustainable future.

Promoting Sustainable Industries

In today's world, promoting sustainable industries has become more crucial than ever. As individuals and communities, we must acknowledge the importance of recycling and its significant impact on our environment. Recycling not only helps reduce waste but also plays a vital role in fostering sustainable industries. This subchapter sheds light on the power of recycling and its ability to transform waste into wonder.

Recycling is a key component in the shift towards a more sustainable future. By recycling materials such as paper, plastics, glass, and metals, we can conserve natural resources and reduce the need for extracting raw materials from the earth. This, in turn, helps to preserve our natural habitats, protect biodiversity, and mitigate climate change. It is a collective responsibility for every one of us to actively participate in recycling efforts.

Promoting sustainable industries goes beyond just recycling at an individual level. It involves supporting and encouraging businesses that adopt environmentally friendly practices. Many industries have already acknowledged the importance of recycling and have incorporated it into their operations. These sustainable industries focus on creating innovative products from recycled materials, minimizing waste generation, and adopting energy-efficient manufacturing processes.

Recycling not only contributes to sustainable industries but also creates numerous job opportunities. As the demand for recycling grows, more workers are needed to collect, sort, process, and produce recycled goods. This industry provides employment opportunities at various skill levels, ranging from manual labor to technical expertise. Promoting sustainable industries not only benefits the environment but also stimulates economic growth and social well-being.

To promote sustainable industries, everyone can play an active role. Individuals can start by adopting recycling practices in their daily lives, separating recyclables from general waste, and supporting local recycling initiatives. Educating ourselves and others about the benefits of recycling is also crucial. By spreading awareness, we can inspire others to take action and promote sustainable industries in their own communities.

In conclusion, promoting sustainable industries is a vital aspect of the recycling movement. By recycling, we can conserve resources, protect the environment, and foster economic growth. It is essential for every one of us to understand the importance of recycling and actively participate in promoting sustainable industries. Together, we can turn waste into wonder and create a greener, more sustainable future for generations to come.

Chapter 5: Recycling Around the World

Successful Recycling Programs and Initiatives

Recycling is an essential practice that benefits not only the environment but also the economy and the overall well-being of communities. Over the years, numerous recycling programs and initiatives have emerged, showcasing the power of recycling and its ability to transform waste into wonder. These successful endeavors serve as inspiration for individuals, businesses, and governments to embrace recycling and contribute to a sustainable future.

One remarkable example is the city of San Francisco's recycling program. Dubbed as one of the most successful in the world, San Francisco has achieved a remarkable 80% waste diversion rate. Through a combination of comprehensive recycling education, strict waste management regulations, and innovative initiatives, the city has set a benchmark for others to follow. San Francisco's success demonstrates that with commitment and determination, even the most ambitious recycling goals can be achieved.

Another notable initiative is the "RecycleBank" program. This innovative program, implemented in various cities across the United States, rewards individuals for their recycling efforts. Participants earn points based on the amount they recycle, which can be redeemed for discounts at local businesses or donated to charitable organizations. By providing incentives, RecycleBank has successfully increased recycling rates and fostered a sense of community engagement in recycling.

In the corporate world, companies such as Patagonia have taken recycling to a whole new level. Patagonia's "Worn Wear" program encourages customers to repair and reuse their clothing rather than purchasing new items. Through a network of repair centers and educational campaigns, the company aims to extend the lifespan of its products and reduce waste. This initiative not only promotes sustainability but also builds customer loyalty by emphasizing the value of long-lasting, high-quality products.

On a global scale, the "Plastic Bank" initiative tackles the issue of ocean pollution caused by plastic waste. This program establishes recycling centers in developing countries, where individuals can exchange collected plastic for essential goods and services. By providing economic incentives for recycling, the Plastic Bank empowers communities to protect the environment while addressing poverty and promoting sustainable development.

These successful recycling programs and initiatives highlight the importance of recycling in creating a more sustainable future. They demonstrate that recycling is not just about waste management but also about economic growth, community engagement, and environmental stewardship. Regardless of our background or profession, we can all contribute to successful recycling programs by embracing the principles of reduce, reuse, and recycle in our daily lives. Together, we can turn waste into wonder and pave the way for a greener, brighter future.

Challenges and Solutions in Developing Countries

In the quest to address the global waste crisis, it is crucial to acknowledge the unique challenges faced by developing countries. These nations often struggle with limited resources, inadequate waste management infrastructure, and a lack of awareness about the importance of recycling. However, despite these obstacles, there are several innovative solutions that can transform these challenges into opportunities for growth and sustainability.

One of the major challenges faced by developing countries is the lack of proper waste management systems. Many of these nations do not have the necessary infrastructure to handle the increasing amount of waste generated by their growing populations. As a result, waste often ends up in landfills, causing environmental pollution and health hazards. The solution lies in the development of efficient waste management systems, such as recycling facilities, composting plants, and waste-to-energy technologies. By investing in these sustainable solutions, developing countries can not only reduce their environmental footprint but also create employment opportunities and boost their economies.

Another challenge is the limited awareness about the importance of recycling among the general public. In many developing countries, people are not aware of the negative impacts of improper waste disposal or the potential benefits of recycling. To address this issue, educational campaigns and community engagement programs are crucial. By raising awareness about the importance of recycling and providing practical guidance on how to incorporate recycling practices into daily life, developing countries can empower their citizens to become active participants in the waste management process.

Furthermore, financial constraints often hinder the implementation of recycling initiatives in developing countries. Lack of funding for recycling infrastructure and technology can hinder progress in waste management. However, partnerships between governments, non-profit organizations, and private sectors can help overcome this challenge. By pooling resources and expertise, these collaborations can drive the development of sustainable recycling solutions and create a circular economy that benefits both the environment and the economy.

In conclusion, developing countries face unique challenges in addressing the waste crisis and promoting recycling. However, with the right strategies and collaborations, these challenges can be transformed into opportunities for growth and sustainability. By investing in waste management infrastructure, raising awareness about recycling, and fostering partnerships, developing countries can harness the power of recycling to create a cleaner and more prosperous future for all.

Global Collaboration for a Sustainable Future

In this modern era, the importance of recycling has become increasingly evident. Recycling is not just a personal responsibility but a global endeavor that requires collaboration from every individual, community, and country. The concept of a sustainable future is not just a buzzword; it is a necessity for the survival of our planet and the well-being of future generations.

The challenges we face in terms of waste management and environmental degradation are immense. Every year, millions of tons of waste end up in landfills and pollute our air, water, and soil. This not only poses a threat to human health but also disrupts ecosystems, leading to the loss of biodiversity and climate change. It is clear that a change in our approach to waste management is urgently needed.

Global collaboration is the key to addressing these challenges effectively. We must recognize that waste knows no boundaries. It is not confined to a single country or region but affects us all. Therefore, a collective effort is required to tackle this global problem. Governments, non-governmental organizations, businesses, and individuals must come together and work towards a common goal – a sustainable future.

At the governmental level, international agreements and policies play a crucial role in promoting recycling and waste reduction. Organizations such as the United Nations and the World Health Organization have established frameworks and guidelines to encourage countries to adopt sustainable waste management practices.

Collaboration between nations is essential to share knowledge, best practices, and resources.

Non-governmental organizations (NGOs) also play a vital role in advancing the importance of recycling. These organizations work tirelessly to raise awareness, provide education, and implement recycling programs in communities around the world. NGOs often collaborate with local governments and businesses to find innovative solutions and promote sustainable practices.

Businesses, too, have a responsibility to contribute to a sustainable future. Many companies are now incorporating recycling and waste reduction into their operations. By adopting eco-friendly practices, they not only reduce their environmental footprint but also inspire others to follow suit. Collaboration between businesses and governments can result in the development of effective recycling infrastructure and the creation of green jobs.

Finally, individuals must recognize their role in global collaboration. Every action, no matter how small, makes a difference. By practicing the three R's – reduce, reuse, and recycle – individuals can significantly contribute to the sustainability movement. Educating ourselves and our communities about the importance of recycling is crucial for long-term change.

In conclusion, global collaboration is essential for a sustainable future. Governments, NGOs, businesses, and individuals must work together to address the challenges of waste management and environmental degradation. By recognizing the importance of recycling and taking concerted action, we can create a better world for ourselves and future generations. Let us join hands and build a future where waste becomes wonder.

Chapter 6: Innovations in Recycling Technology

Advanced Sorting and Processing Techniques

In today's world, where the importance of recycling has become increasingly evident, advanced sorting and processing techniques have emerged as powerful tools in the battle against waste. These innovative methods have revolutionized the recycling industry, offering efficient solutions that help us transform waste into wonder.

Sorting and processing waste materials is a crucial step in the recycling process, as it enables the separation of various recyclable components from the rest of the waste. Advanced sorting techniques have greatly enhanced this process, allowing for a more accurate and efficient segregation of different materials. One such technique is automated sorting, which uses cutting-edge technology to identify and separate recyclables based on their physical and chemical properties. This method not only saves time and labor but also ensures a higher quality of recycled materials.

Advanced processing techniques, on the other hand, focus on transforming the sorted waste into valuable resources. One notable example is mechanical recycling, which involves breaking down plastic waste into smaller particles and then reusing them to produce new plastic products. This technique significantly reduces the need for raw materials and helps to conserve our precious natural resources.

Another remarkable advancement in waste processing is chemical recycling. This technique involves converting plastic waste back into its original chemical building blocks, which can then be used to produce new plastics or other materials. Chemical recycling offers a promising solution for recycling plastics that are currently difficult to recycle, such as mixed or contaminated plastics.

Additionally, advanced sorting and processing techniques have paved the way for the development of energy recovery systems. These systems convert non-recyclable waste into energy, such as electricity or heat. By harnessing the energy potential of waste, we can reduce our dependence on fossil fuels and contribute to a more sustainable future.

The integration of advanced sorting and processing techniques in the recycling industry has not only increased the efficiency of recycling operations but also expanded the range of materials that can be recycled. Today, we can recycle not only paper, glass, and plastic but also electronic waste, batteries, and even organic waste. This broadened scope further highlights the importance of recycling in preserving our planet's resources and reducing our environmental footprint.

In conclusion, the advancements in sorting and processing techniques have revolutionized the recycling industry, enabling us to transform waste into wonder. These advanced methods offer efficient and effective solutions for segregating and processing various materials, leading to a higher quality of recycled products. By embracing these techniques, we can contribute to a more sustainable future and ensure that the power of recycling continues to inspire wonder for generations to come.

Creative Upcycling and Repurposing Ideas

In this subchapter, we will explore the fascinating world of creative upcycling and repurposing ideas. Recycling is undoubtedly vital for our environment, but what if we could take it a step further and transform waste into something truly wonderful? This is where the concept of upcycling and repurposing comes into play.

Upcycling is the process of converting discarded materials into something of higher value and quality. It involves repurposing items that would typically end up in landfills and giving them a new lease on life. By upcycling, we not only reduce waste but also promote resourcefulness and creativity.

One fantastic idea for upcycling is turning old wine bottles into beautiful decorative vases. By simply removing the labels and adding a fresh coat of paint, you can transform an ordinary glass bottle into a stunning centerpiece. Another idea is repurposing wooden pallets into unique furniture pieces or even vertical gardens. With a little bit of sanding and staining, those discarded pallets can become the focal point of your living room or a thriving oasis for your plants.

Perhaps you have an old, worn-out suitcase lying around. Instead of throwing it away, why not repurpose it into a vintage-inspired pet bed? Add some cushions, a cozy blanket, and voila! Your furry friend will have a stylish and comfortable resting place. Another idea for repurposing is transforming empty tin cans into charming candle holders. By punching holes in the metal and adding a tea light, you can create a warm and inviting ambiance in your home.

Upcycling and repurposing ideas are limited only by your imagination. You can turn old fabric scraps into unique patchwork quilts or transform broken ceramic plates into mosaic art pieces. The possibilities are endless, and the process is both fulfilling and rewarding.

By embracing upcycling and repurposing, we not only contribute to the importance of recycling but also unleash our creativity and give new life to discarded items. These ideas not only help reduce waste but also add a touch of uniqueness and personality to our surroundings.

So, why not embark on an upcycling adventure today? Explore your attic, basement, or garage, and you might just stumble upon hidden treasures waiting to be transformed. Join the growing community of upcyclers and repurposers, and together, let's turn waste into wonder.

Emerging Technologies and Future Possibilities

In the ever-evolving world of recycling, emerging technologies are playing a crucial role in transforming waste into wonder. As we strive to create a sustainable future, these advancements bring forth exciting possibilities that have the potential to reshape our world and contribute to a cleaner environment.

One of the most promising technologies on the horizon is the development of advanced sorting systems. Traditional recycling methods heavily rely on manual sorting, which can be time-consuming and prone to errors. However, with the integration of artificial intelligence and machine learning, automated sorting systems are becoming increasingly efficient and accurate. These advanced technologies can identify and separate different materials, such as plastic, glass, and paper, at an unprecedented speed, thereby streamlining the recycling process and increasing its effectiveness.

Another emerging technology with immense potential is chemical recycling. While traditional recycling processes focus on mechanical methods, chemical recycling takes a different approach by breaking down waste materials at a molecular level. Through innovative techniques like pyrolysis and depolymerization, chemical recycling can convert various types of waste, including plastics that are traditionally hard to recycle, into valuable raw materials. This breakthrough technology not only offers a solution to the growing plastic waste crisis but also presents an opportunity to create a circular economy where waste is transformed into new products.

Furthermore, advancements in renewable energy technologies are enabling waste-to-energy conversion. Instead of sending waste to landfills, cutting-edge technologies such as anaerobic digestion and gasification can convert organic waste into biogas or syngas, which can be used to generate electricity, heat, or even biofuels. By harnessing the energy potential of waste, we can reduce our dependence on fossil fuels and mitigate the environmental impact of traditional energy sources.

The future possibilities of recycling are not limited to technological advancements alone. As individuals and communities become more conscious of the importance of recycling, innovative initiatives are emerging to promote a circular economy. From upcycling workshops to community composting programs, these grassroots efforts are fostering a culture of sustainability and encouraging creative solutions to waste management.

In conclusion, emerging technologies offer a glimmer of hope in transforming waste into wonder. With advanced sorting systems, chemical recycling, and waste-to-energy conversion, we have the tools at our disposal to create a more sustainable future. However, it is essential for individuals, communities, and industries to embrace these technologies and work collectively towards a world where recycling becomes the norm. By doing so, we can unlock the full potential of recycling and pave the way for a cleaner, greener, and more harmonious planet for generations to come.

Chapter 7: Recycling at Home and in the Community

Setting up an Effective Recycling System at Home

Recycling has become an essential practice in today's world, as we strive to protect the environment and conserve valuable resources. While many of us are aware of the importance of recycling, we often struggle with implementing an effective recycling system at home. In this subchapter, we will explore some practical tips and guidelines to help you set up a successful recycling system in your own household.

First and foremost, it is crucial to understand the importance of recycling. Recycling not only reduces the amount of waste sent to landfills but also conserves energy and natural resources. By recycling, we can minimize pollution, combat climate change, and protect the delicate ecosystems that surround us. Therefore, setting up an effective recycling system at home is not just a personal responsibility, but a collective effort towards a sustainable future.

To begin, familiarize yourself with the recycling guidelines in your area. Different municipalities have different rules and regulations when it comes to recycling. Educate yourself about what can and cannot be recycled, as well as the correct way to prepare and sort your recyclables. This knowledge will help you avoid contamination and ensure that your recycling efforts are meaningful.

Next, designate a specific area in your home for recycling. Set up separate bins or containers for different types of materials, such as paper, plastic, glass, and metal. Make sure these containers are easily accessible and clearly labeled. This will not only make it convenient for you and your family to recycle, but also encourage everyone to participate actively.

Furthermore, establish a routine for recycling collection. Create a schedule for emptying and disposing of your recyclables. Whether it is weekly, bi-weekly, or monthly, stick to the plan to maintain a consistent recycling practice. Additionally, consider joining a local recycling program or consulting with waste management companies that offer recycling services. They can provide you with recycling bins and pick up your recyclables, making the process even more streamlined.

Finally, lead by example and educate others about the importance of recycling. Encourage your family members, friends, and neighbors to join you in your recycling efforts. Share information about the benefits of recycling and inspire others to make a positive impact on the environment.

In conclusion, setting up an effective recycling system at home is a crucial step towards making a difference in the world. By following the guidelines mentioned in this subchapter, you can contribute to a cleaner and healthier planet. Remember, every small action adds up, and together, we can transform waste into wonder through the power of recycling.

Engaging Schools and Local Organizations in Recycling

One of the most effective ways to promote and encourage recycling is by engaging schools and local organizations in the process. Schools play a crucial role in educating and shaping young minds, making them perfect platforms for instilling the importance of recycling and environmental consciousness.

By incorporating recycling programs into school curriculums, students are not only taught about the significance of recycling but also gain practical knowledge on how to implement it in their daily lives. Schools can organize workshops, seminars, and interactive sessions to educate students about the benefits of recycling, the proper sorting of waste, and the impact it has on the environment. This not only empowers them with knowledge but also helps in fostering a sense of responsibility towards the planet.

Furthermore, schools can also establish recycling clubs or committees, where students can actively participate in recycling initiatives. These clubs can organize various activities such as waste audits, where students analyze the type and volume of waste generated in the school. Based on these audits, they can then devise strategies to minimize waste and promote recycling within the school premises. Additionally, schools can collaborate with local recycling facilities and waste management companies to provide students with hands-on experiences, such as visits to recycling plants or waste sorting centers. This exposure will not only enhance their understanding of the recycling process but also encourage them to become ambassadors of recycling in their communities.

Apart from schools, local organizations also play a vital role in promoting recycling. Businesses, community centers, and non-profit organizations can actively participate in recycling campaigns and initiatives. These organizations can organize recycling drives, where they collect specific items such as electronics, paper, or plastic, and ensure their proper disposal or recycling. By working together, these organizations can create a collective impact, raising awareness and motivating individuals to recycle.

Engaging schools and local organizations in recycling is essential as it not only educates and empowers individuals but also creates a ripple effect within communities. The knowledge and practices gained through these initiatives can be easily shared with families and friends, further expanding the impact of recycling. By involving everyone, from students to local businesses, we can create a culture of recycling that transcends generations and becomes an integral part of our daily lives. Together, we can transform waste into wonder and build a sustainable future for our planet.

Promoting a Culture of Sustainability

In today's rapidly evolving world, it has become increasingly crucial to promote a culture of sustainability. As individuals, communities, and businesses, we must recognize the importance of recycling and actively contribute to preserving our planet for future generations. In this subchapter, we delve into the significance of recycling and how it contributes to creating a sustainable future.

Recycling is a vital tool in tackling the global waste crisis. By transforming waste into valuable resources, we can reduce the strain on our environment and minimize the need for extraction of new raw materials. Recycling helps conserve energy, water, and other natural resources, thereby reducing our carbon footprint and mitigating the harmful effects of climate change.

One of the primary reasons recycling is crucial is its impact on reducing landfill waste. Landfills not only take up precious land, but they also release harmful greenhouse gases into the atmosphere. By recycling, we divert waste from landfills and alleviate the burden on our ecosystems. It is estimated that recycling just one ton of paper saves approximately 17 trees, 7,000 gallons of water, and 4,000 kilowatts of energy.

Furthermore, recycling helps stimulate the economy by creating jobs and fostering innovation. Recycling industries require a skilled workforce to collect, sort, process, and distribute recycled materials. By supporting these industries, we not only contribute to the well-being of our planet but also create employment opportunities and boost economic growth.

Promoting a culture of sustainability goes beyond individual efforts. It requires collective action and involvement from all sectors of society. Governments, businesses, and educational institutions play a crucial role in educating people about recycling and implementing policies that support sustainable practices. By working together, we can establish a comprehensive recycling infrastructure that makes recycling easily accessible for everyone.

To promote a culture of sustainability, it is essential to raise awareness about recycling and its benefits. Educational programs, community initiatives, and media campaigns can help disseminate knowledge and inspire individuals to adopt recycling as a way of life. By emphasizing the positive impact recycling has on the environment, we can encourage a shift in attitudes and behaviors towards a more sustainable future.

In conclusion, promoting a culture of sustainability is paramount in our quest to protect the environment and build a better future. Recycling not only helps alleviate the strain on our planet's resources but also creates economic opportunities and fosters innovation. By working together and embracing recycling as a way of life, we can transform waste into wonder and make a significant positive impact on our planet.

Chapter 8: Overcoming Barriers to Recycling

Lack of Awareness and Education

In our modern world, the importance of recycling cannot be overstated. It is a crucial step towards sustainable living and preserving our planet for future generations. However, one of the main obstacles we face in achieving widespread recycling is the lack of awareness and education. This subchapter aims to shed light on this issue and highlight the need for increased knowledge and understanding about recycling.

In many parts of the world, recycling is still seen as an optional activity, rather than a responsibility. This mindset stems from a lack of awareness about the detrimental effects of waste accumulation on the environment. People often fail to realize that their small daily actions, such as tossing a plastic bottle into the regular trash bin, can have significant long-term consequences. By highlighting the impact of waste on our ecosystems, this subchapter aims to awaken readers to the urgency of recycling.

Furthermore, lack of education is another significant barrier to effective recycling. Many individuals are simply unaware of the proper methods for recycling different types of materials or the locations of recycling centers in their communities. As a result, they may inadvertently contaminate recycling streams, rendering the efforts of others futile. This subchapter will provide practical tips and guidelines on how to recycle correctly, empowering readers to become active participants in the recycling process.

The importance of education is not limited to individuals but extends to businesses as well. Many companies still operate without prioritizing sustainability and recycling practices. By showcasing the economic benefits of recycling, such as reduced waste disposal costs and the creation of green jobs, this subchapter aims to encourage businesses to integrate recycling into their operations. It will also emphasize the positive impact this can have on their brand image and customer loyalty.

Ultimately, increasing awareness and education about recycling is crucial for fostering a culture of sustainability. By spreading knowledge and understanding, every individual can become a catalyst for change. This subchapter will provide the necessary tools and resources to help readers incorporate recycling into their daily lives, empowering them to make a positive impact on the environment. Together, we can transform waste into wonder and build a greener, more sustainable future for all.

Addressing Behavioral and Attitudinal Challenges

Recycling is undoubtedly a crucial aspect of modern society, with far-reaching implications for the environment, economy, and future generations. However, despite its importance, we still face significant behavioral and attitudinal challenges when it comes to recycling. In this subchapter, we will delve into these challenges and explore effective strategies to address them.

One of the primary hurdles we face is the lack of awareness and understanding surrounding the importance of recycling. Many people still perceive recycling as a tedious and time-consuming task, failing to recognize the positive impact it can have on our planet. Therefore, it is vital to educate individuals about the significance of recycling, emphasizing the environmental benefits, resource conservation, and reduction in landfill waste.

Another behavioral challenge we encounter is the resistance to change. People are often resistant to deviating from their established routines, even if it means making a positive difference. Overcoming this challenge requires a shift in mindset and the promotion of a recycling culture. By highlighting success stories and showcasing the positive impact of recycling, we can inspire individuals to embrace change and adopt recycling as a daily habit.

Attitudinal challenges also play a significant role in hindering recycling efforts. Some individuals believe that their individual actions won't make a difference or that recycling is solely the responsibility of the government or large corporations. To counter this attitude, it is crucial to emphasize the collective impact of individual actions and highlight the power of community involvement. By fostering a sense of collective responsibility, we can motivate individuals to actively participate in recycling initiatives.

Additionally, convenience and accessibility are key factors influencing recycling behaviors. Lack of access to recycling facilities or limited recycling options can discourage individuals from participating. Therefore, it is essential to improve infrastructure and make recycling more accessible to everyone. This can be achieved through the implementation of comprehensive recycling programs, community drop-off centers, and the integration of recycling facilities into public spaces.

In conclusion, addressing behavioral and attitudinal challenges is essential for promoting the importance of recycling. By increasing awareness, fostering a culture of recycling, emphasizing collective responsibility, and improving accessibility, we can overcome these challenges and encourage widespread participation. Together, we can harness the power of recycling and transform waste into wonder, creating a sustainable future for all.

Policy and Legislative Support for Recycling Efforts

In order to fully comprehend the importance of recycling, it is crucial to understand the role of policy and legislative support in driving recycling efforts. Governments around the world have recognized the urgent need to address waste management and have implemented various policies and laws to encourage and regulate recycling practices.

One of the primary objectives of policy and legislative support is to establish a framework that encourages responsible waste management and recycling. Governments have realized that relying solely on individual efforts and voluntary initiatives is not sufficient to tackle the global waste crisis. Therefore, they have taken the initiative to develop comprehensive waste management strategies that include recycling as a core component.

These policies often include mandates and targets for recycling rates, which serve as an incentive for businesses and individuals to actively participate in recycling efforts. By setting specific goals, governments encourage the adoption of recycling practices and create a sense of urgency to address the growing waste problem.

Moreover, policy and legislative support also extends to the development of infrastructure and facilities for recycling. Governments have invested in recycling plants, sorting centers, and waste management facilities to ensure the efficient collection, separation, and processing of recyclable materials. By providing the necessary infrastructure, governments facilitate the recycling process and make it more convenient for individuals and businesses to participate.

Furthermore, policies and legislation also play a crucial role in fostering innovation and technological advancements in the recycling industry. Governments often provide financial incentives and grants to researchers and businesses involved in developing new recycling technologies. This support stimulates the creation of more efficient and sustainable recycling methods, leading to improved waste management practices and reduced environmental impact.

In addition to these direct measures, policy and legislative support also includes raising public awareness about the importance of recycling. Governments invest in educational campaigns and outreach programs to inform and educate the public about the benefits of recycling and the consequences of improper waste disposal. By promoting a culture of recycling, governments aim to instill sustainable habits in individuals from a young age, ensuring a long-term commitment to recycling efforts.

In conclusion, policy and legislative support are vital in driving recycling efforts and addressing the waste management challenges faced by the world today. Through the implementation of targeted policies, governments encourage responsible waste management, establish recycling targets, develop infrastructure, foster innovation, and raise public awareness. By working together and supporting recycling initiatives, we can transform waste into wonder and create a sustainable future for generations to come.

Chapter 9: Inspiring Stories of Recycling Success

Individuals Making a Difference

In the grand scheme of things, it's easy to feel overwhelmed by the enormity of the world's environmental challenges. Climate change, pollution, and resource depletion can seem insurmountable. However, it is crucial to remember that change starts with individuals. Each and every one of us has the power to make a difference through the simple act of recycling.

Recycling is not just about separating our waste into different bins or dropping off items at recycling centers. It is a powerful tool that transforms waste into wonder, giving new life to materials that would otherwise end up in landfills or polluting our oceans. It is a process that starts with individuals like you and me, making conscious choices in our everyday lives.

By recycling, we contribute to the conservation of resources. Many products we use, such as paper, plastics, and metals, can be recycled and turned into new items. This reduces the need for extracting raw materials from the Earth, which often results in habitat destruction and air and water pollution. When we recycle, we help preserve natural resources for future generations.

Recycling also plays a significant role in reducing greenhouse gas emissions. When waste decomposes in landfills, it releases methane, a potent greenhouse gas that contributes to climate change. By diverting waste from landfills through recycling, we can reduce the amount of methane released into the atmosphere. Additionally, recycling requires less energy compared to producing new materials from scratch, leading to further reductions in carbon emissions.

The impact of recycling is not limited to the environment; it extends to our economy and communities as well. Recycling creates jobs in the collection, sorting, and processing of recyclable materials. It promotes local economic growth and provides opportunities for entrepreneurs to develop innovative recycling technologies. Moreover, recycling helps create a cleaner and healthier environment for our communities, reducing pollution and improving overall quality of life.

The importance of recycling cannot be overstated. It is a small but significant step towards addressing the global environmental crisis. By taking responsibility for our waste and making conscious choices to recycle, we become part of a larger movement that seeks to build a sustainable future.

So, let us remember that we hold the power to make a difference. Each time we recycle, we contribute to conserving resources, reducing greenhouse gas emissions, and building a better world for ourselves and future generations. From waste to wonder, recycling empowers individuals to be agents of positive change. The choices we make today can shape a brighter and more sustainable tomorrow.

Businesses Leading the Way

In today's world, where environmental concerns are at the forefront of global discussions, businesses are increasingly recognizing the importance of recycling and taking proactive steps to lead the way towards a more sustainable future. From small local enterprises to multinational corporations, companies across various industries are embracing recycling initiatives and making significant contributions to the cause.

One of the key reasons businesses are stepping up their recycling efforts is the growing realization that waste management is not just an ethical obligation but also a smart business strategy. By implementing effective recycling programs, companies can reduce their environmental footprint and cut costs simultaneously. Recycling not only helps conserve natural resources but also enables businesses to gain a competitive edge by improving their overall sustainability performance.

Numerous businesses have incorporated recycling into their core operations, effectively demonstrating that profitability and sustainability can go hand in hand. For instance, manufacturing companies have started using recycled materials as inputs for their production processes, thereby reducing their reliance on virgin resources. This not only reduces the amount of waste generated but also helps conserve energy and minimize greenhouse gas emissions.

Retailers are also playing a crucial role in promoting recycling through various initiatives. Many large retail chains have implemented take-back programs, allowing customers to return their used products for recycling. This not only ensures proper disposal of potentially harmful materials but also encourages customers to actively participate in the recycling process.

Furthermore, businesses are embracing innovative recycling technologies to transform waste into valuable resources. Companies are investing in state-of-the-art equipment and facilities to efficiently process and recycle different types of materials, such as plastics, paper, and metals. These innovative approaches not only divert waste from landfills but also create new revenue streams by turning waste into valuable raw materials for other industries.

However, it's not just large corporations that are leading the way in recycling. Small and medium-sized enterprises (SMEs) are also making significant contributions to the cause. Many SMEs actively participate in community recycling programs, partnering with local organizations to promote recycling and educate the public about its importance. These efforts not only benefit the environment but also enhance the reputation and goodwill of these businesses within their communities.

In conclusion, businesses across all sectors are increasingly recognizing the importance of recycling and are taking proactive steps to lead the way towards a more sustainable future. By incorporating recycling into their core operations, investing in innovative technologies, and actively engaging with communities, businesses are demonstrating that profitability and sustainability can go hand in hand. With businesses leading the way, the power of recycling is being harnessed to transform waste into wonder, creating a brighter and greener future for every one.

Community-driven Recycling Initiatives

In this subchapter, we will explore the incredible potential of community-driven recycling initiatives and their significance in addressing the global waste crisis. Recycling is not just a responsibility of governments and corporations; it is a collective effort that requires active participation from every individual. By embracing recycling initiatives at the community level, we can bring about significant positive change and contribute to a more sustainable future.

Community-driven recycling initiatives are grassroots movements that empower local residents to take charge of their waste management. These initiatives involve organizing recycling programs, creating awareness campaigns, and establishing networks to collect and process recyclable materials. They are driven by the belief that small actions can make a big difference in preserving our environment.

One of the key advantages of community-driven recycling initiatives is their ability to foster a sense of ownership and responsibility among participants. When individuals actively engage in recycling activities within their communities, they become more conscious of their consumption patterns and waste generation. This heightened awareness leads to a shift in behavior, with people opting for more eco-friendly choices and reducing their overall waste output.

Moreover, community-driven recycling initiatives have a direct impact on local economies. By establishing recycling centers and supporting local businesses involved in recycling, these initiatives create job opportunities and stimulate economic growth. They also contribute to the development of a circular economy, where waste materials are transformed into valuable resources, reducing the need for raw materials extraction.

These initiatives also serve as platforms for education and awareness. Through workshops, seminars, and community events, individuals can learn about the importance of recycling, the environmental consequences of improper waste disposal, and the various methods of waste reduction. By sharing knowledge and experiences, community members can inspire and motivate others to join the recycling movement, creating a ripple effect that extends beyond individual households.

In conclusion, community-driven recycling initiatives play a vital role in addressing the global waste crisis. By encouraging active participation and fostering a sense of ownership, these initiatives empower individuals to make a positive impact on their environment. They not only contribute to waste reduction but also stimulate local economies and foster a culture of sustainability. The power of recycling lies within each and every one of us, and by coming together as a community, we can transform waste into wonder.

Chapter 10: The Future of Recycling

Innovations and Breakthroughs on the Horizon

The world of recycling is constantly evolving, and there are exciting innovations and breakthroughs on the horizon that hold the potential to transform our approach to waste management. These advancements not only address the growing concerns around the importance of recycling but also pave the way for a more sustainable and eco-friendly future for all.

One area of innovation that is gaining traction is the development of advanced recycling technologies. Traditional recycling methods often face limitations when it comes to certain types of materials, such as plastics and electronics. However, researchers and scientists are now exploring cutting-edge techniques that can break down these challenging materials, enabling their conversion into valuable resources.

For instance, chemical recycling is a promising breakthrough that involves the use of specialized processes to convert plastic waste into its basic building blocks, which can then be used to manufacture new plastic products. This method has the potential to significantly increase the recycling rates of plastics that are currently considered non-recyclable, reducing the amount of plastic waste that ends up in landfills or pollutes our oceans.

Another exciting development in the recycling field is the rise of innovative recycling technologies that harness renewable energy sources. These technologies not only recycle waste but also generate clean energy in the process. For example, waste-to-energy plants utilize advanced combustion or gasification techniques to convert organic waste into electricity or heat, reducing the need for fossil fuels and minimizing greenhouse gas emissions.

Furthermore, the advent of smart recycling systems is set to revolutionize waste management. These systems employ sensors and data analysis to optimize waste collection, making it more efficient and cost-effective. By monitoring waste levels in real-time, these systems can ensure that bins are emptied when necessary, reducing overflowing bins and improving the overall cleanliness of communities.

In conclusion, the world of recycling is witnessing remarkable innovations and breakthroughs that have the potential to revolutionize waste management as we know it. From advanced recycling technologies to renewable energy generation and smart recycling systems, these advancements address the importance of recycling and pave the way for a more sustainable future. It is crucial for everyone to stay informed and involved in these developments, as they have the power to transform waste into wonder and create a cleaner, greener planet for future generations.

Shifting Towards a Circular Economy

In recent years, there has been a growing recognition of the importance of recycling and the need to transition towards a circular economy. This subchapter explores the concept of a circular economy and its significance in our efforts to transform waste into wonder.

A circular economy is an alternative to the traditional linear economy, where resources are extracted, used, and disposed of. In a circular economy, the aim is to minimize waste and maximize the value of resources by keeping them in use for as long as possible. This concept promotes the idea of recycling and reusing materials, reducing the need for new resource extraction and minimizing the environmental impact of production and consumption.

The shift towards a circular economy holds multiple benefits for all of us. Firstly, it helps to conserve natural resources. By recycling and reusing materials, we reduce the need to extract new resources from the earth, which in turn helps to preserve our forests, minerals, and fossil fuels. This is crucial for the long-term sustainability of our planet and the well-being of future generations.

Secondly, embracing a circular economy can lead to job creation and economic growth. Recycling and reusing materials require a workforce, from collection and sorting to processing and manufacturing. By investing in recycling infrastructure and promoting circular practices, we can create green jobs and stimulate local economies.

Additionally, a circular economy promotes innovation and technological advancements. Finding new ways to recycle and reuse materials often requires creative thinking and the development of new technologies. This drive for innovation can lead to breakthroughs in waste management and resource efficiency, ultimately benefiting not only the environment but also businesses and consumers.

Moreover, a circular economy contributes to reducing greenhouse gas emissions and mitigating climate change. The extraction, production, and disposal of goods are major contributors to carbon emissions. By extending the lifespan of products through recycling and reusing, we can significantly reduce the carbon footprint associated with their production and disposal.

As individuals, we can contribute to the shift towards a circular economy by embracing recycling in our daily lives, supporting sustainable businesses, and advocating for policies that promote circular practices. By doing so, we can play an active role in preserving resources, creating a greener economy, and securing a sustainable future for our planet.

In conclusion, shifting towards a circular economy is not just a necessity but an opportunity. It allows us to transform waste into wonder, conserve natural resources, create jobs, foster innovation, and mitigate climate change. By understanding the importance of recycling and embracing circular practices, we can all be part of this transformative journey towards a more sustainable and prosperous future.

Creating a Sustainable Legacy for Future Generations

In a world grappling with environmental challenges, it is crucial for every one of us to understand the significance of recycling and the role it plays in creating a sustainable legacy for future generations. Recycling is not merely a buzzword; it is a powerful tool that can transform waste into wonder. This subchapter aims to shed light on the importance of recycling and how it can positively impact our planet and the lives of those who inhabit it.

Recycling is fundamentally important because it conserves our natural resources. By reusing materials instead of extracting new ones, we reduce the need for mining and deforestation, thereby preserving our forests and habitats. Through recycling, we can protect our valuable ecosystems, maintain biodiversity, and ensure that future generations can enjoy the wonders of nature as we do today.

Moreover, recycling helps mitigate the adverse effects of climate change. The production of goods from raw materials often results in high emissions of greenhouse gases. By recycling, we can significantly reduce these emissions and combat global warming. Recycling also plays a crucial role in reducing energy consumption, as it requires less energy to produce goods from recycled materials compared to virgin resources. By embracing recycling, we can contribute to a cleaner and healthier planet for future generations.

In addition to environmental benefits, recycling has significant economic advantages. The recycling industry creates jobs and stimulates economic growth. It presents opportunities for innovation and entrepreneurship, as new technologies and processes emerge to handle different types of waste. By actively participating in recycling initiatives, we can foster a circular economy that promotes sustainable growth and prosperity for all.

To ensure a sustainable legacy, education and awareness are key. It is essential for every one of us to understand the importance of recycling and actively participate in recycling programs. By learning about the materials that can be recycled, separating waste appropriately, and supporting recycling initiatives in our communities, we can make a profound difference. Encouraging others to recycle and sharing our knowledge can amplify the impact, creating a ripple effect that benefits our planet and future generations.

In conclusion, creating a sustainable legacy for future generations requires a collective effort. By embracing the importance of recycling, we can conserve natural resources, mitigate climate change, stimulate economic growth, and leave behind a planet that is vibrant and full of wonder. Let us each play our part in this journey towards sustainability, ensuring that our actions today shape a better tomorrow for every one.

Conclusion: Empowering Change through Recycling

In this captivating journey of exploring the power of recycling, we have delved into the importance of recycling and its impact on our planet. From Waste to Wonder: The Power of Recycling has aimed to raise awareness and empower individuals from all walks of life to actively participate in the global movement of recycling.

Recycling is not just a responsibility; it is a privilege that each one of us possesses. It is an opportunity to make a difference, to protect our environment, and to create a sustainable future for generations to come. By embracing recycling, we can transform waste into wonder, turning what was once considered useless into valuable resources.

The importance of recycling cannot be overstated. It is a crucial step towards reducing our carbon footprint, conserving natural resources, and mitigating the harmful effects of climate change. Through recycling, we can minimize the need for raw materials extraction, which often leads to deforestation, habitat destruction, and pollution. By reusing and repurposing materials, we can significantly reduce the amount of waste that ends up in landfills and incinerators, preventing further damage to our ecosystems.

But recycling is not just about saving the planet; it is also about creating economic opportunities and promoting social change. The recycling industry has the potential to generate millions of jobs worldwide, from waste management and sorting to manufacturing and innovation. Recycling can alleviate poverty, empower communities, and foster a sense of collective responsibility. It is a powerful tool that can bridge the gap between economic growth and environmental stewardship.

To fully harness the power of recycling, it is essential for every individual to understand their role in this global movement. By adopting simple habits like separating recyclables from non-recyclables, reducing single-use plastics, and supporting local recycling initiatives, we can each make a tangible impact. Education and awareness are key, as they empower us to make informed choices and inspire others to do the same.

From Waste to Wonder: The Power of Recycling aims to inspire change, not only in our behavior but also in our mindset. It invites everyone, regardless of their background or niche, to become agents of change. By embracing recycling, we can transform our world into a place where waste is no longer seen as a burden, but as a valuable resource waiting to be unlocked.

Let us unite and empower change through recycling. Together, we can create a brighter, more sustainable future for ourselves, our children, and the generations to come. The power is in our hands, and the wonders that await are limitless.

Milton Keynes UK
Ingram Content Group UK Ltd.
UKHW021814010124
435297UK00016B/920